BALLADS · POP · ROCK · SOUL · JAZZ · SHOWS · FILMS · CLASSICAL

AUDITION SOURCEBOOK: Female Singers

A COLLECTION OF 22 SONGS

Covering eight different vocal styles.
Arranged for piano, voice and guitar with sound-alike
backing tracks on 2 CDs.

Published by
Wise Publications
8/9 Frith Street, London W1D 3JB, England.

Exclusive Distributors:
Music Sales Limited
Distribution Centre, Newmarket Road, Bury St Edmunds, Suffolk IP33 3YB, England.
Music Sales Pty Limited
120 Rothschild Avenue, Rosebery, NSW 2018, Australia.

Order No. AM90116
ISBN 0-7119-3182-8
This book © Copyright 2005 Wise Publications,
a division of Music Sales Limited.

Compiled by Lucy Holliday.
Printed in the EU.

CDs recorded, mixed & mastered by Jonas Persson.
Piano by Paul Honey.
Backing vocals by Alison Symons & Elly Barnes.

WISE PUBLICATIONS

part of The Music Sales Group
London / New York / Paris / Sydney / Copenhagen / Berlin / Madrid / Tokyo

BALLADS

BEAUTIFUL: 4

In E♭ major

THE CLOSEST THING TO CRAZY: 9

In E major

FROM A DISTANCE: 14

In G major

POP

FAMILY AFFAIR: 19

In G♯ minor

MURDER ON THE DANCEFLOOR: 24

In E major

TOXIC: 31

In C minor

ROCK

COMPLICATED: 38

In D minor

DON'T SPEAK: 44

In C minor

BLACK VELVET: 50

In E♭ minor

SOUL

MIDNIGHT TRAIN TO GEORGIA: 57

In D♭ major

(TAKE A LITTLE) PIECE OF MY HEART: 62

In E♭ major

SON OF A PREACHER MAN: 65

In E major

JAZZ

AIN'T GOT NO – I GOT LIFE: 70

In G major

**FLY ME TO THE MOON
(IN OTHER WORDS): 75**

In D minor

SHOOT THE MOON: 86

In C major

SHOWS

CABARET: 89

In B♭ major

ON MY OWN: 98

In G minor

TELL ME IT'S NOT TRUE: 104

In F major

FILMS

ONE DAY I'LL FLY AWAY: 108

In D minor

**THERE ARE WORSE THINGS
I COULD DO: 112**

In E minor

CLASSICAL

POOR WANDERING ONE: 116

In A♭ major

**TAKE ME TO YOUR HEART AGAIN
(LA VIE EN ROSE): 124**

In G major

BALLADS

POP

ROCK

SOUL

JAZZ

SHOWS

FILMS

CLASSICAL

BEAUTIFUL

Words & Music by Linda Perry

THE CLOSEST THING TO CRAZY

Words & Music by Mike Batt

How can hap - pi - ness feel so wrong?
It's so ea - sy to break a heart.

How can mi - se - ry feel so sweet?
It's so ea - sy to close your eyes.

How can you let___ me watch___ you sleep then
How can you treat___ me like a child_____ yet

break my dreams___ the way___ you do?_____
like a child___ I yearn___ for you?_____

FROM A DISTANCE

Words & Music by Julie Gold

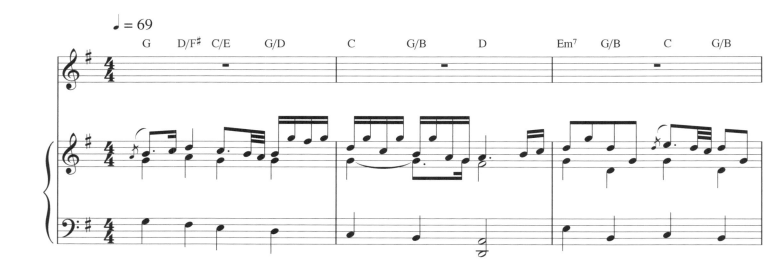

1. From a dis-tance the world_ looks blue_ and green,_ and the
(Verses 2 & 3 see block lyric)

snow - capped_ moun - tains white. From a dis - tance the o - cean meets_

Verse 2:
From a distance we all have enough
And no one is in need.
And there are no guns, no bombs and no disease
No hungry mouths to feed.
For a moment we are instruments
Marching in a common band
Playing songs of hope, playing songs of peace
They're the songs of every man.

Verse 3:
From a distance you look like my friend
Even though we are at war.
From a distance I just cannot comprehend
What all this fighting is for.
From a distance there is harmony
And it echoes through the land
And it's the hope of hopes, it's the love of loves
It's the heart of every man.

FAMILY AFFAIR

Words & Music by Mary J. Blige, Bruce Miller, Andre Young, Camara Kambon,
Mike Elizondo, Melvin Bradford, Asiah Louis & Luchana Lodge

beat, your prob-lem not mine. Leave all that B. S. out -side, we are gon-na ce -le -brate all night. Let's have

fun to - night, no fights. Turn that great track way up high. Mak - ing you dance all night and I got some

D.%.
Repeat chorus to fade

real heat for you this time. It does-n't mat -ter if you're white or black, let's get crunk 'cos Ma- ry's back.

Verse 2:
It's only gonna be about a matter of time
Before you get loose and start to lose your mind
Cop you a drink, go 'head and rock your ice
'Cause we celebrating No More Drama in our life
With a great track pumpin', everybody's jumpin'
Go ahead and twist your back and get your body bumpin'
I told you leave your situations at the door
So grab somebody and get your ass on the dance floor.

Let's get it crunk, we gon' have fun up on it   *etc.*

MURDER ON THE DANCEFLOOR

Words & Music by Gregg Alexander & Sophie Ellis-Bextor

burn this god - damn house right down. It's   mur - der on the dance - floor_____

Verse 2:
Oh, I know, I know, I know, I know, I know, I know, I know
There may be others
And so, and so, and so, and so, and so, and so, and so
You'll just have to pray.
If you think you're getting away
I will prove you wrong
I'll take you all the way
Stay another song, I'll blow you all away.

Hey, it's murder on the dancefloor *etc.*

TOXIC

Words & Music by Cathy Dennis, Christian Karlsson,
Pontus Winnberg & Henrik Jonback

1. Ba - by, can't you see   I'm call - ing,_____   a guy like you

should wear a warn - ing._____ It's dan - ge - rous, I'm fall - ing._____

2. There's no es - cape, I can't wait._____ I need a hit, ba - by, give me it._____
3. It's get - ting late to give you up._____ I took a sip from my dev - il's cup._____

You're dan - ger - ous, I'm lov - ing it._____
Slow - ly, it's tak - ing ov - er me._____

COMPLICATED

Words & Music by Avril Lavigne, Lauren Christy,
David Alspach & Graeme Edwards

DON'T SPEAK

Words & Music by Eric Stefani & Gwen Stefani

-ing, don't tell me 'cause it hurts.

Don't speak, I know what you're think - in', I don't need your rea-

-sons, don't tell me 'cause it hurts. Old

me-mo-ries, they can be in-vit-ing but some are

You and me,—

I can see— us dy - ing, aren't— we?——————

Repeat with ad lib. vocals - 4° fade

Don't speak, I know— just what— you're say - in', so— please stop— ex - plain-
(hurts.)

49

BLACK VELVET

Words & Music by Christopher Ward & David Tyson

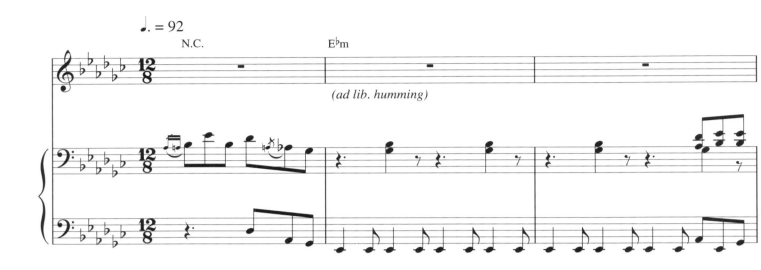

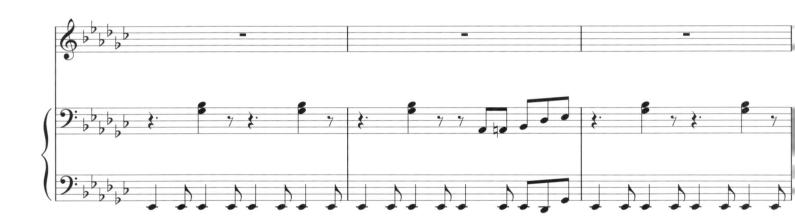

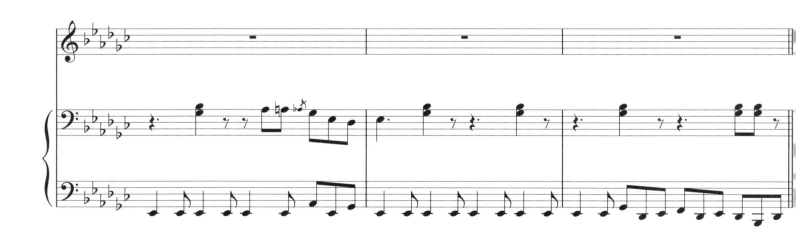

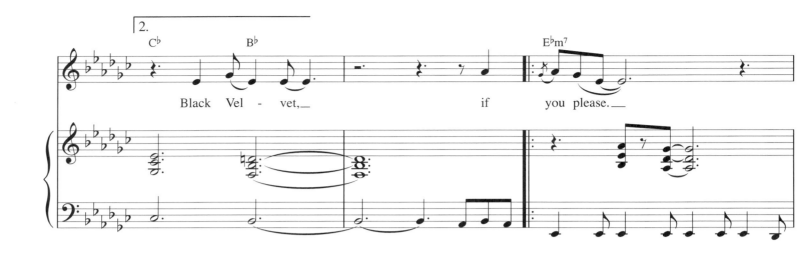

Black Vel - vet,＿ if you please.＿

Repeat ad lib. to fade

Verse 2:
Up in Memphis, the music's like a heatwave
White lightning, bound to drive you wild.
Mama's baby is in the heart of every schoolgirl
"Love Me Tender" leaves 'em crying in the aisle.
The way he moved, it was a sin, so sweet and true.
Always wanting more, he'd leave you longing for...

Black Velvet *etc*.

MIDNIGHT TRAIN TO GEORGIA

Words & Music by Jim Weatherly

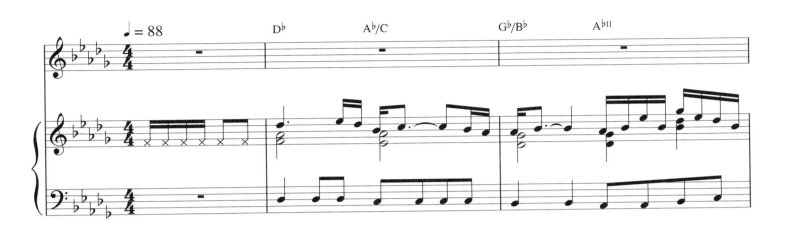

1. Mm_____ L. A.___
(Verse 2 see block lyric)

proved_____ too much for the man. (Too much for the man,___ he could-n't

SOUL

place and time.   Oh yes he is.   And I'll
(When - ev - er he takes that ride guess who's gon - na be right by his side.)

— be with him (I know you will) on that mid - night train to Geor -

- gia.   Hey.
(Leav - in' on the mid - night train to Geor - gia, woo woo!)

I'd ra - ther live in his world, than live with - out him in mine.
(live in his world)   (Her world is

his,   his and hers_ a-lone.)   (Her   world   is his,   his and hers_ a-lone)

in mine._   Hey!_____

Repeat to fade

Oh   love,   gon-na board   the mid-night   train to go.
(Oh   love,   gon-na board   the mid-night   train to go)

Verse 2:
He kept dreamin' that someday he'd be the star
(A superstar, but he didn't get far)
But he sure found out the hard way
That dreams don't always come true
So he turned all his hopes
And he even sold his old car
Bought a one-way ticket back to the life he once knew.

He's leavin' *etc*.

(TAKE A LITTLE) PIECE OF MY HEART

Words & Music by Jerry Ragovoy & Bert Berns

Verse 2:
You're out on the street (looking good)
And you know deep down in your heart that ain't right
And oh, you never hear me when I cry at night
I tell myself that I can't stand the pain
But when you hold me in your arms I say it again.

So come on *etc.*

SON OF A PREACHER MAN

Words & Music by John Hurley & Ronnie Wilkins

1. Bil - ly Ray was a preach - er's son_ and when his
(Verse 2 see block lyric)

dad - dy was preach - ing he'd come_ a - long;   when they ga - thered round and start - ed talk - ing

SOUL

Verse 2:
Being good isn't always easy
No matter how hard I try.
When he started sweet talking to me,
He'd come and tell me everything is all right,
He'd kiss and tell me everything is all right,
Can't get away again tonight.

AIN'T GOT NO - I GOT LIFE

Words & Music by Galt MacDermot, James Rado & Gerome Ragni

FLY ME TO THE MOON
(IN OTHER WORDS)

Words & Music by Bart Howard

Fly me to the moon let me play a - mong the stars

let me see___what spring is like on Jup-i-ter and Mars___ in oth-er___ words hold my hand,

in oth-er words dar-ling kiss me.___

Fill my life with song___ let me___ sing for ev-er more.

76

SHOOT THE MOON

Words & Music by Jesse Harris

Verse 2:
Now the fall is here again
You can't begin to give in, its all over
When the snows come rolling through
You're rolling too with some new lover
Will you think of times you've told me
That you knew the reason
Why we had to each be lonely?
It was just the season.

Verse 3:
(Instrumental)
Will you think of times you've told me
That you knew the reason
Why we had to each be lonely?
It was just the season.

CABARET

Words by Fred Ebb
Music by John Kander

SHOWS

when I saw her laid out like a queen, she was the hap-pi-est corpse I'd ev-er seen. I think of Els-ie to this ve-ry day. I re-mem-ber how she'd turn to me and say:

ON MY OWN
(FROM "LES MISÉRABLES")

Music By Claude-Michel Schönberg

Original Lyrics by Alain Boublil & Jean-Marc Natel

English Lyrics by Herbert Kretzmer, Trevor Nunn & John Caird

And now I'm all a - lone a - gain; no - where to go, no one to turn to.

I did not want your mo - ney, sir, I came out here 'cause I was told to. And now the night is

near; now I can make be - lieve— he's here.

Some - times I walk a - lone at night, when ev -'ry - bo - dy else is sleep - ing.

I think of him and then I'm hap - py with the com - pa - ny I'm keep - ing.

The ci - ty goes to

TELL ME IT'S NOT TRUE

Words & Music by Willy Russell

Rather slow

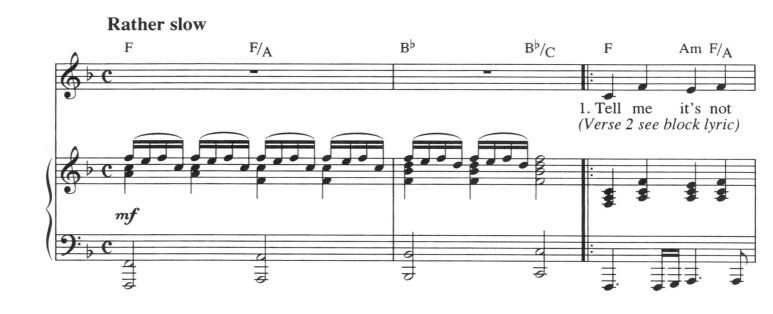

1. Tell me it's not
(Verse 2 see block lyric)

true. Say it's just a sto - ry Some-thing in the news.

Tell me it's not true, though it's here be-

say it's just the end__ of an old mo-vie of years__ a - go;

from an old mo-vie with Ma-ri-lyn Mon - roe.__

molto rall.

Verse 2

Say it's just some clowns,
Two players in the limelight
And bring the curtain down.
Say it's just two clowns
Who couldn't get their lines right,
Say it's just a show on the radio
That we can turn over and start again,
We can turn over, it's only a game.

SHOWS

ONE DAY I'LL FLY AWAY

Words by Will Jennings
Music by Joe Sample

One day I'll fly a - way leave all this to yes - ter - day.__

What more__ could your love do for me, when will love be through with me?

Why live life from dream to dream, and dread the day when

FILMS

dream - ing   ends.

One day I'll fly___ a - way___   leave all this to

THERE ARE WORSE THINGS I COULD DO

Words & Music by Jim Jacobs & Warren Casey

Freely, colla voce

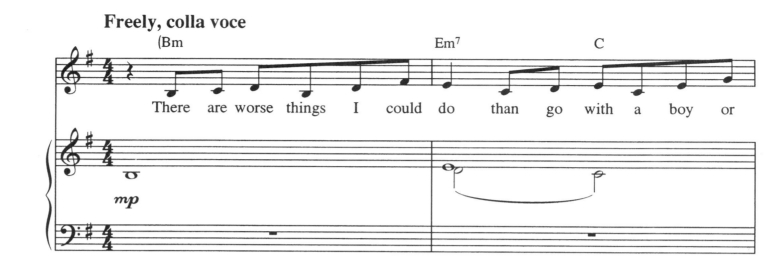

There are worse things I could do than go with a boy or

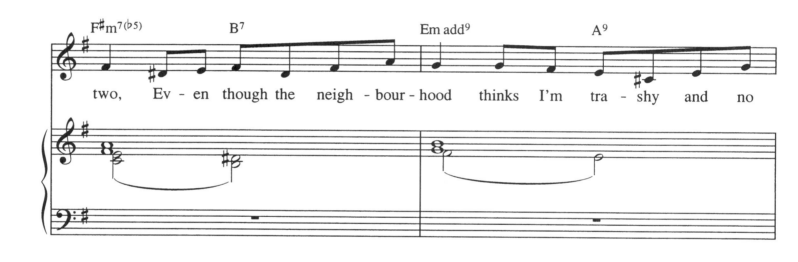

two, Ev - en though the neigh - bour - hood thinks I'm tra - shy and no

good; I sup - pose it could be true, but there are worse things I could

POOR WANDERING ONE

Words by W.S.Gilbert
Music by Sir Arthur Sullivan

one!_____ Poor wan - d'ring one!_____

If such poor love____ as mine____

Can help thee find true peace of mind; Why, take____ it,

it____ is thine! Take heart,

no dan - ger low'rs; Take an - y heart; ___ but

ours! Take heart, fair days will shine; ___ Take

an - y heart; take mine! Take

Chorus

heart, no dan - ger low'rs; Take _____ an - y

heart;___ but ours! Take heart, fair days will

shine;___ take an - y heart; take mine! Ah!_____

Ah!_____ Ah!_____

Ah!_____

ah!

Ah, ah! Ah, ah, ah!

Fair days will shine,

Take heart!

Take_____ mine! Take_____ heart!

TAKE ME TO YOUR HEART AGAIN
(LA VIE EN ROSE)

Words by Edith Piaf
Music by R.S.Louiguy

Il me l'a dit me l'a ju - ré_____ pour la vi - e. Et dès que je a - per-

ev - 'ry day words seem to turn_____ in - to love songs. Give your heart and soul to

-çois, a - lors je sens en moi, mon coeur qui bat.

me and life will al - ways be la vie en rose.

Des yeux qui font bais - ser les miens, un rire qui se perd sur sa bouch

His eyes make me___ look___ down his laugh loo - ses it - self on his mouth,

2 3 4 5 6 7 8 9
2/06(57974)